Based on an original idea by Alex A.

First published in French in 2012 by Presses Aventure under the title
Opération Moignons.

© Alex A. and Les Publications Modus Vivendi Inc., 2016
All rights reserved. No part of this publication may be reproduced, stored
in a retrieval system or transmitted, in any form or by any means without
the publisher's written authorization.

Published by **Adventure Press**, an imprint of:
Les Publications Modus Vivendi Inc.
55 Jean-Talon Street West
Montreal, Quebec, Canada H2R 2W8
www.adventurepress.ca

Publisher: Marc G. Alain
Editorial Director: Marie-Eve Labelle
Author and illustrator: Alex A.
Page layout: Vicky Masse
Translator: Rhonda Mullins

Legal deposit – Bibliothèque et Archives nationales du Québec, 2016
Legal deposit – Library and Archives Canada, 2016

ISBN 978-2-89751-189-0 (PAPERBACK)

ISBN 978-2-89751-233-0 (PDF)
ISBN 978-2-89751-234-7 (EPUB)
ISBN 978-2-89751-235-4 (KINDLE)

We gratefully acknowledge the financial support of the Government
of Canada through the Canada Book Fund (CBF) for our publishing activities.

Government of Québec – Tax credit for book publishing – Administered by SODEC

Printed in Canada in April 2016

OPERATION SHORTHAND

WRITTEN AND ILLUSTRATED BY ALEX A.

ADVENTURE PRESS

FOR LAURENCE,
WHO HELPS ME DiSCOVER
THE TRUE NATURE OF
MY CHARACTERS.

MA'AM, I FOUND THE CREATURE. I'M GOING TO TRY TO CAPTURE HIM.

GREAT. BE VERY CAREFUL, SHORTHAND. IT ALREADY DISMEMBERED THREE OF OUR AGENTS.

I'LL BE FINE.

WHERE ARE YOU HIDING?...

BEEP BEEP

SHORTHAND...

8

AND FLOPPY! THE MOST TALENTED HACKER ON THE PLANET.

PLEASED TO MEET YOU.

ISN'T HE THE CUTEST THING?!!

JUST LOOK AT HIS LITTLE MUZZLE!

HEE HEE HEE!

HERE WE GO AGAIN...

AS YOU KNOW, 20 EGGS HAVE BEEN HIDDEN ACROSS THE CONTINENT.

IT'S UP TO YOU TO FIND THEM.

YOU CAN USE ANY EQUIPMENT THE AGENCY PROVIDES. X-RAY GLASSES, JET PACKS, PRETTY MUCH ANYTHING YOU NEED.

THE ONE WHO FINDS THE MOST EGGS WINS.

AND WHAT DO WE WIN THIS YEAR?

A DATE WITH BILLY. DINNER AND A MOVIE, AND THEN WHO KNOWS?

HI THERE!

HELLO!

YOU HAVE 24 HOURS TO COMPLETE THE CHALLENGE. SO...

... LET THE **GAMES BEGIN!**

SHE CAN BE VERY THEATRICAL WHEN SHE WANTS TO!

FOUND ONE!

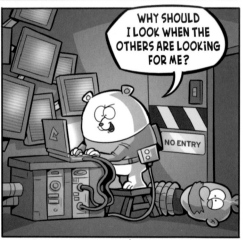

WHY SHOULD I LOOK WHEN THE OTHERS ARE LOOKING FOR ME?

NO ENTRY

HEE HEE! THIS ISN'T SO HARD.

HEY!

YESSS! ANOTHER ONE.

EXCUSE ME, I BELIEVE I SAW IT FIRST...

OH! UM, YES, OF COURSE, HERE!

BEEP BEEP

YES!

THEY'RE EVERYWHERE!

CALL FOR REINFORCEMENTS!

GOOD GOD!

MA'AM, WE HAVE A PROBLEM. IT SEEMS THAT OUR AGENTS ARE UNDER ATTACK!

DOES IT LOOK SERIOUS?

THEY GOT MY ARM!

FOR YEARS, WHITEWASH WAS ONE OF THE AGENCY'S MOST FEARSOME ENEMY.

HE'S ALWAYS BEEN FIXATED ON THE IDEA OF PLAYING GOD AND CREATING THE ULTIMATE BEING.

TO DO THIS, HE WOULD STEAL DIFFERENT BODY PARTS FROM GIFTED PEOPLE ON THE PLANET. SOME OF THEM WERE OUR AGENTS...

I'M A BIT FUNNY IN THE HEAD!

LIKE AGENT GERALD...

AGENT CONRAD

AGENT RUFUS

AND OF COURSE...

AHHH, GOTCHA!

BUT ALL OF THESE CREATIONS WERE FAILURES. THE ONLY THING HE MANAGED TO CREATE WERE HORRIBLE, BLOODTHIRSTY MONSTERS.

LUCKILY, OVER 15 YEARS AGO, WHITEWASH WAS CAPTURED BY ONE OF OUR AGENTS AND HELD IN BUILDING C IN THE PACIFIC SECTOR, WHERE HE RECEIVED TREATMENT FROM THE BEST PSYCHIATRIST ON THE PLANET, DR. JULIUS.

HOLD ON, HOLD ON... THE AGENCY HAS MORE THAN ONE BUILDING?

OF COURSE. WE HAVE ONE FOR EACH SECTOR OF THE PLANET.

... WHY DOESN'T ANYONE HERE TELL ME ANYTHING?

WHITEWASH UNDERWENT 10 YEARS OF INTENSIVE THERAPY.

DR. JULIUS MANAGED TO DISCOVER HIS DEEPEST, DARKEST SECRETS, AND HE WAS REINTEGRATED INTO SOCIETY.

23

24

WOW. HE'S IN A BAD MOOD.

WHITEWASH MUST HAVE REMOVED HIS CHIP, THAT'S ALL.

NO HE DIDN'T. COME ON. HE DOESN'T EVEN KNOW HE HAS ONE. NOT TO MENTION THAT IT WAS IMPLANTED AT THE CENTRE OF HIS BRAIN. REMOVING IT WOULD HAVE KILLED HIM!

WHAT IF WE SPOKE TO DR. JULIUS? HE KNOWS WHITEWASH INSIDE AND OUT. MAYBE HE KNOWS SOMETHING.

THAT'S NOT POSSIBLE...

... THERE WAS... AN INCIDENT.

5 YEARS EARLIER...

GOOD GOD!

SCRATCH

BLOOP BLOOP

SORRY, SHORTHAND. THERE'S NOTHING WE CAN DO.

WITHOUT YOUR HANDS YOU CAN'T GO ON MISSIONS ANYMORE. TAKE A FEW WEEKS TO THINK ABOUT WHAT YOU WANT TO DO.

ANOTHER JOB...

I DON'T WANT ANOTHER JOB...

SHORTHAND!

AH! JON! WHAT ARE YOU DOING HERE?

YOU WANT TO PLAY WITH ME? I LOST MY SOCKS, AND WE HAVE TO GO OUT ON A MISSION TO FIND THEM!

29

FOR AN EVEN MORE DRAMATIC EFFECT, PLAY THE THEME FROM *JURASSIC PARK*. (YOU KNOW, THE BIT THAT GOES "TA TA TA TAAA TATATA TATA TA TAAAAAA.")
WELCOME TO BUILDING C. IT'S NICE TO SEE YOU AGAIN, MR. SHORTHAND.

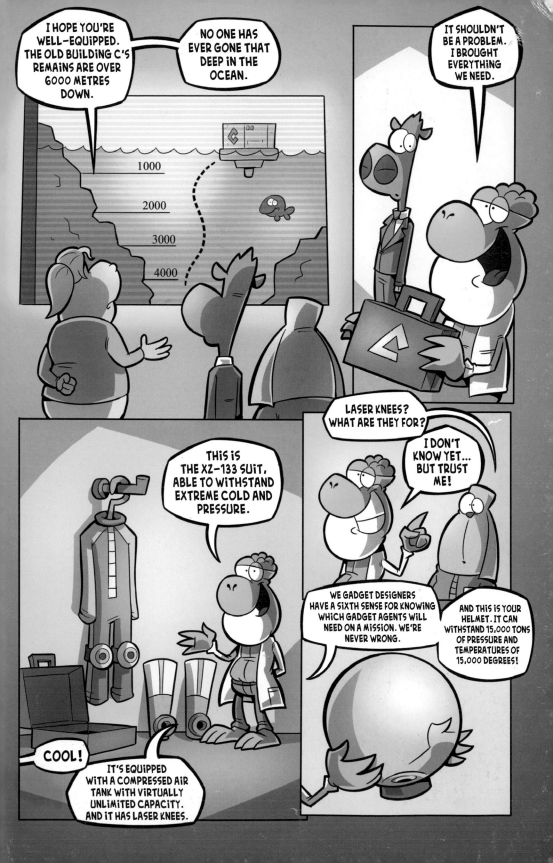

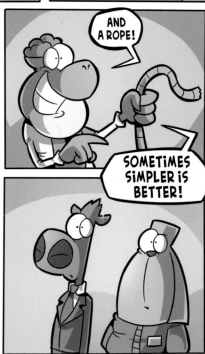

34

35

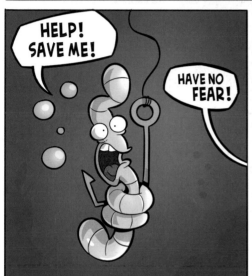

39

40

SHORTHAND! WHAT ARE YOU DOING HERE!?

TOW

ARE YOU OKAY, SHORTHAND? YOU'RE ALL PUFFED UP!

OH, RIGHT. WE'RE UNDERWATER. UM, YOU'D BETTER GET IN MY HELMET, BUT THERE'S NOT A LOT OF ROOM...

MMMM!!

OH!

SO, DO YOU KNOW WHERE WE'RE SUPPOSED TO GO?

OF COURSE. I KNOW THIS PLACE INSIDE AND OUT. THIS IS WHERE I WORKED BEFORE I LOST MY HANDS. FOLLOW ME.

YOU OKAY?

YES, YES...

WOW, THIS IS QUITE A PLACE!

DR. JULIUS
PSYCHIATRIST

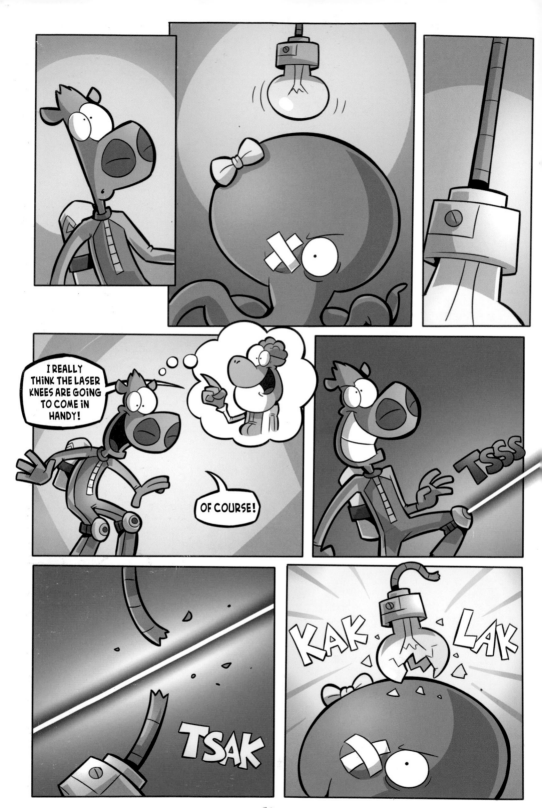

50

BUT!...

IT'S ALRIGHT. LET ME HANDLE THIS. I'M GOING TO USE...

PSYCHOLOGY.

OCTOPUS, WHY ARE YOU ATTACKING US? ARE YOU ACTING OUT BASED ON HOW YOU WERE TREATED WHEN YOU WERE YOUNG?

BLOOP, BLOOPBLOOP BLOOP, BLOOP, BLOOP...

HMMM, VERY INTERESTING...

TELL ME ABOUT YOUR MOTHER.

52

THAT WASN'T THE PROBLEM. ROCKS ARE PRETTY STABLE. HE MUST HAVE GONE INSANE AFTER WORKING AS A GUINEA PIG IN A LAB...

THAT DOESN'T EXPLAIN WHY HE'S OBSESSED WITH THE IDEA OF CREATING THE ULTIMATE BEING!

THAT'S ALWAYS BEEN SOMETHING OF A MYSTERY.

TOP SECRET

PATIENT: WHITEWASH
FINAL REPORT

HEY! LOOK AT THIS! THERE ARE DRAWINGS OF HIM TOO.

JON, WE'RE NOT INTERESTED IN THOSE SORTS OF DETAILS!

BUT LOOK! IT'S REALLY CUTE.

WHITEWASH

UM, YES, WHATEVER...

LOOK, THIS ONE IS THE ONLY ONE WHERE HE'S SMILING.

LET'S SEE.

ACCORDING TO THE GPS CHIP, WHITEWASH ISN'T ANYWHERE ON EARTH...

WHITEWASH

IS IT POSSIBLE THAT...

BILLY! POINT THE SATELLITE AT THE MOON. LOOK FOR SIGNS OF LIFE.

YES, MA'AM

THERE! SOMEONE'S THERE!

ARGH! LEAVE ME ALONE, WOULD YOU!!

NO, NOT HIM. OVER THERE.

HELLO THERE, AGENCY FOLKS!

WELL DONE! YOU DID YOUR HOMEWORK. A GOOD HIDEOUT, ISN'T IT?

UM... HOW CAN YOU BREATHE?

AH, I BROUGHT MY OWN PERSONAL OXYGEN SUPPLY. DON'T WORRY.

PUFF *PUFF*

ALL IN A DAY'S WORK!

PUFF *PUFF*

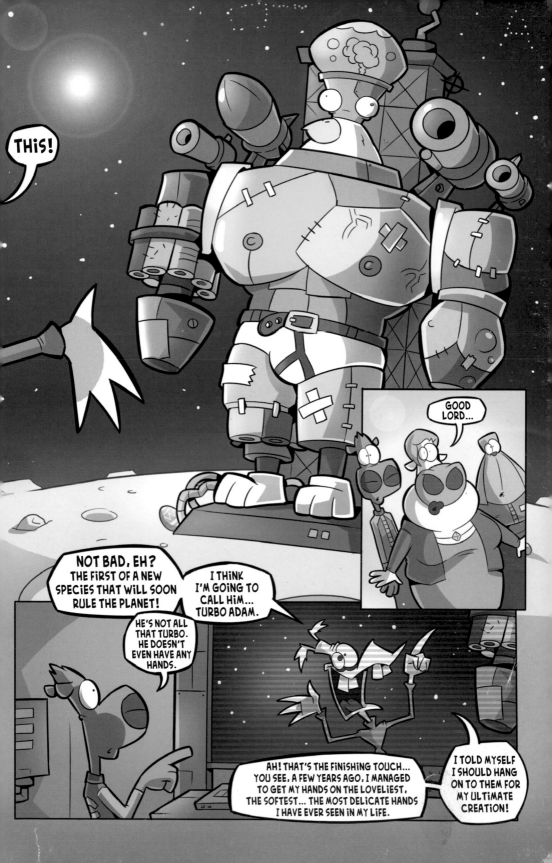

PRETTY, AREN'T THEY?

HE HAS MY HANDS...

VOILÀ! ALL I NEED IS A LITTLE LUNAR STORM TO BRING IT TO LIFE IN A THEATRICAL FASHION.

UM, THE MOON DOESN'T HAVE STORMS...

YES IT DOES! I'VE SEEN THEM.

NO, THERE'S NO SUCH THING.

VERY WELL. WE'LL TEST IT WITH AN APPLE. BILLY, POINT THE RAY AT THE MOON.

COOL!

CHECK THE CONDITION OF THE APPLE.

I'M AWAITING CONFIRMATION.

YES, THE MOLECULAR STRUCTURE OF THE APPLE IS INTACT. YOU CAN GO.

COOL! I'M GOING.

NO, I'LL GO FIRST. I'M THE ONE WHO SHOULD TAKE THE RISK.

OKAY THEN...

65

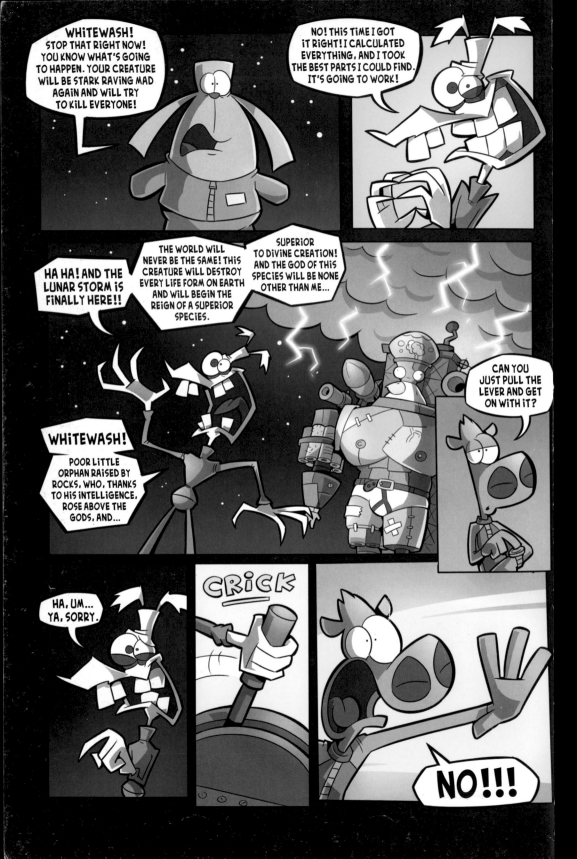

IT'S ALIVE!!
IT'S ALIVE!!

TURBO ADAM,
I AM YOUR
CREATOR.
HOW DO
YOU FEEL?

SPEAK.

... WHERE'S THE TV? THE GAME IS ABOUT TO START.

WHAT'S HE TALKING ABOUT?

WHAT'S HE DOING? I DON'T UNDERSTAND!!!

HE SHOOTS, HE SCORES!

YEAH! THEY WON!

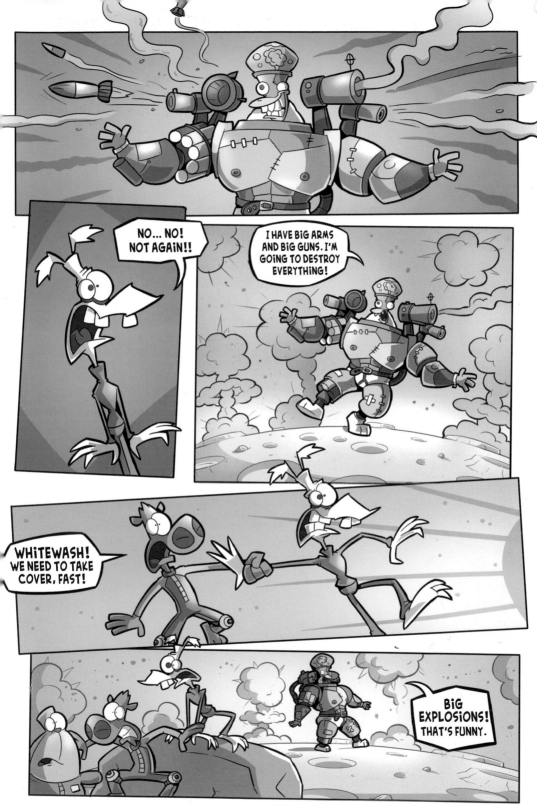

71

72

TA DA DAAAAA!!!

IT'S THE TWO OF US NOW!

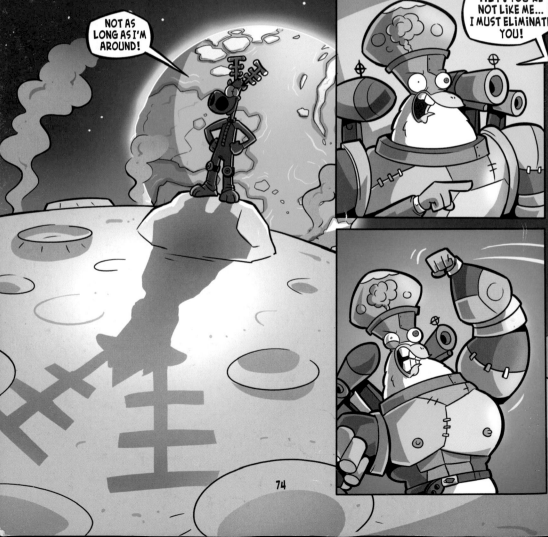

74

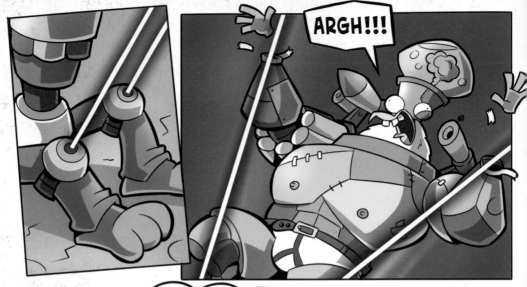

WAAW!

TURBO ADAM IS OUT OF COMMISSION.

SO ALL'S WELL THAT ENDS WELL!

YEP.

IT'S WEIRD... I FEEL LIKE SOMETHING IS MISSING. DON'T YOU?

YEP, IT'S LIKE... A LITTLE TOO QUIET.

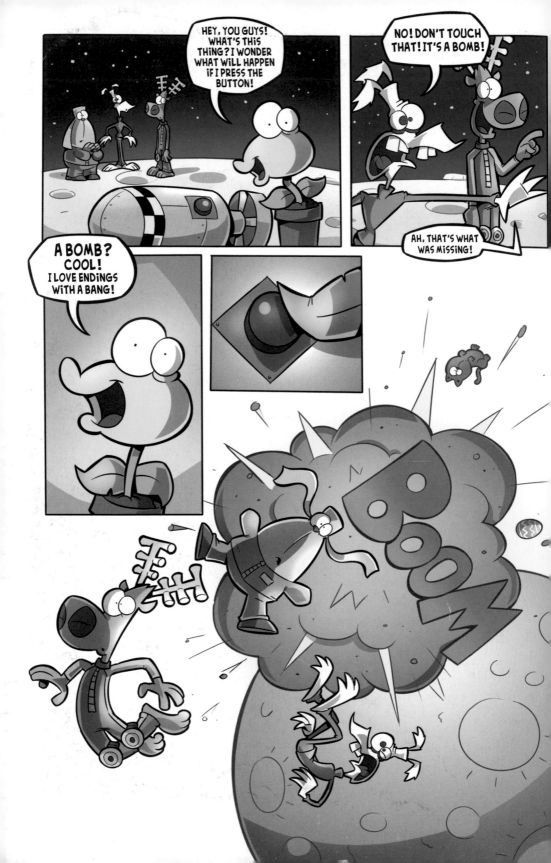

85

YOU GOT HIM, JON

NO...

WE GOT HIM!

MR. SHORTHAND! ARE YOU OKAY?!

UM... YES, YES... I THINK SO.

OOF! THAT WAS AN EXPLOSIVE ENDING!

YES... LUCKILY YOU WERE THERE TO SAVE THE DAY, AS USUAL!

THE END

TOP SECRET

FILE NO. 48
PATIENT: WHITEWASH

EARTH A

You've probably noticed that the Earth featured in the *Super Agent Jon Le Bon* series isn't quite like the one we know. That's because it's not exactly our Earth.

All the characters I create, including Jon Le Bon, live in the same world. And a lot of them live on what I call "Earth A": a planet with three continents, where humans, animals, mutants, extraterrestrials and anyone else I can dream up all live together.

Here's the map with the locations of the Agency's buildings. Jon Le Bon lives in Building A, and that's where most of the action takes place. But little by little in future volumes, I will take you to visit the other buildings, along with parts of the world where they're located!

Of course, there are also top-secret buildings hidden away on this planet.

But I can't talk about them for now!

Did you notice?

TWENTY eggs were hidden in the book, starting on page 17. The Agency's **EGG HUNT** isn't just for agents!

Can you find them all?

Give it a try and then check your answers online at:

alexbd.com/eggchallenge.html

POOR WHITEWASH...

PICK UP WHAT'S LEFT OF HIM.

HE COULD STILL BE USEFUL TO ME.

AND GET READY...

... FOR PHASE 4.

Alex A. is both author and illustrator of *Super Agent Jon Le Bon*. He discovered his love for drawing and creating cartoon characters at the early age of eight and has been at it ever since. His limitless imagination allows him to create new plots and twists and even completely new universes for his wacky and offbeat characters to evolve.

He'll tell you that his main source of inspiration is "all that exists but especially all that doesn't exist but lives in my imagination."

He's been successful as a freelance illustrator for books and magazines but his drive and determination has gotten him where he really wants to be – developing and drawing his own series.

The creation of Jon Le Bon is the culmination of many years of work, and gives us a series that is both very unique, intriguing and totally hilarious. Jon Le Bon, because of his innocence and fearlessness, can get himself in all sorts of trouble – but there's nothing he can't handle with a little help from his friends.

Alex A. lives in Montreal with his dog Wolfy and always shows up for book signings in his distinctive wool hat and colorful plaid pants, ready to entertain his young readers.

Follow Jon Le Bon in his
next big adventure:
THE PROPHECY OF 4

alexbd.com

SUPER AGENT JON LE BON!

A COMIC BOOK SERIES THAT'S FUNNY, OFFBEAT AND BRILLANT!

THE BRAIN OF THE APOCALYPSE

FORMULA V

OPERATION SHORTHAND

THE PROPHECY OF FOUR

TIME TRAVEL MACHINE

A SHEEP IN THE HEAD